A New L[eaf]

When Angu meets the Bu[ddha]

Written by **Tok Meng Haw**

Art by **Jade Fang**

There was once a happy village where everyone was kind and friendly. Nobody locked their doors, and the children would come out to play all day.

The children's joy and laughter filled the air and brought such happiness to everyone. Even the trees seemed to sway to the laughter of the children.

However, one day a man named Angu appeared in the village, and everything changed.

He was big, strong and fierce. He would hide in the forest nearby and attack anyone who came near him. No one was spared, not even the children!

Many people tried to stop him, but no one could. He was too strong and fast.

The once happy village was now filled with fear. The doors were locked, and no children could come out to play.

People said that Angu was from a faraway land, that he was once a kind and gentle person. But under the influence of a bad teacher, Angu had become cruel and started harming people.

This terrible news reached the Buddha, and he felt that he needed to help. So the Buddha set off to find the village and to find Angu.

People loved the Buddha, and many tried to stop him. "Surely Angu will hurt you," they said.

But the Buddha's compassion was great, and he carried on with his journey.

After a few days of walking, the Buddha reached the village. He found people were overcome with fear. All the doors were locked. No one dared to come out, not even to greet him!

The Buddha went straight to the forest to look for Angu.

Taking the loneliest path, the Buddha walked slowly, hoping that Angu would approach him.

Indeed, when Angu saw the Buddha, he picked up his weapon and charged straight at him.

Now, the strangest thing happened.

Although the Buddha was walking slowly and calmly, Angu was not able to catch him. No matter how fast Angu ran, the Buddha remained out of reach.

After a long chase, the exhausted Angu could run no further.

He dropped to the ground wearily and shouted to the Buddha to stop.

At this point, the Buddha turned around and said to Angu kindly, "I have stopped, Angu. It is you who should stop."

"What do you mean, you have stopped?" Angu said. "I couldn't catch you even though I was running as fast as I could. Surely you must be running very fast."

The Buddha replied, "I've stopped hurting people, but you continue to do so. Ahimsaka, it is now time for you to stop too."

Ahimsaka was the name that Angu's parents had given him – it meant "harmless".

Hearing his name again reminded Angu of his parents and their love. He realised that his parents would be very sad if they knew what a cruel person he had become.

Tears streamed down his face as he realised that he had done many bad things.

Angu knew that the Buddha must be very wise. He threw away his weapon and bowed before the Buddha. "Thank you for showing me the way!" Angu said. "You are so wise. Will you be my teacher?"

"You are willing to learn from your mistakes," The Buddha
replied with a smile. "Of course I would be happy
to be your teacher and teach you the Dhamma."

Angu became a monk under the Buddha's guidance, and the
village was saved.

Angu followed what the Buddha taught, and became a kind and gentle monk.

However, he was not happy. When he was alone, Angu often thought about the bad things he had done in the past, and that made him very sad.

When he went on his alms round, many villagers would not give him food. Some villagers even threw stones at him and chased him away. They were angry with Angu for all the bad things that he had done in the past.

Because of this, Angu was never at peace. The Buddha knew about this and waited for the right moment to help.

Early one morning, the Buddha and Angu went to the village for their alms round. As they were walking, they heard the sound of a woman crying in pain.

They followed the cries and came to a house.

They spoke to
a man from the
house and learned
that the woman
was his wife.
She was having
difficulty giving
birth.

The baby was facing the wrong way and would not come out.
Both mother and child had been in pain for many hours.

The Buddha then said to Angu, "Go, Angu. Tell the mother that since your birth, you have not hurt anyone. By this truth, may she and her child be well."

Angu replied, "How can I say that? I've hurt so many people in my life!"

The Buddha then said, "In that case, Angu, tell the mother that since becoming a monk, you have not hurt anyone. By this truth, may she and her child be well."

Angu followed the Buddha's
instruction and uttered those
words. Miraculously, the delivery
went smoothly, and both mother
and child were well.

News of how Angu had saved the mother and child spread quickly throughout the village. People were overjoyed.

The villagers realised that Angu had indeed turned over a new leaf. From then on, everyone treated Angu kindly.

Angu also learned that everybody makes mistakes. He should not feel sad, so long as he was willing to change and be good.

Having found peace of mind, Angu was able to learn the Buddha's teachings quickly. Soon he became a very wise and kind monk himself.

This was how the Buddha, through wisdom and kindness, helped Angu turn over a new leaf.

About the Book

"A New Leaf" is based on a story found in the Buddhist scriptures (Angulimala Sutta MN 86). It is well-known among many Buddhists and in this children's book, I tried to stay close to the original story even as I adapted it for our young audience.

The Angulimala Sutta also featured the King of Kosala, whom after being pressured by his subjects to act, led an army to hunt down Angulimala. Angulimala's mother, upon hearing the news, went in search of her son to try to save him. Meanwhile Angulimala, who was close to fulfilling his teacher's wish of killing a thousand people, saw his mother walking down a path and thought of taking the life of his own mother!

It was at this point that the Buddha intervened and saved Angulimala's mother and quite possibly Angulimala himself. One can begin to see why this story is so popular among the Buddhist community!

People like the story for different reasons. Some people are attracted to the miracles found in the story, others feel that the story reaches a climax when Angulimala puts away his sword and becomes a disciple of the Buddha. My favorite scene occurs near the end of the story where Angulimala realises that despite all the bad deeds he had done in the past, he can still forgive himself if he learns to be better. This is a lesson we can all learn ourselves and offer to others.

I hope both parents and children will enjoy how the story is told in this book.
Lastly, in many traditional Buddhist countries in Southeast Asia as well as Sri Lanka, the Angulimala Paritta is chanted during child birth, as a means to sooth the mother-to-be as well as facilitate safe delivery.

The beautiful verses of the chant go like this:

Yato'haṁ bhaginiariyāyajātiyājāto,

Nābhijānāmi sañciccapāṇaṁjīvitāvoropetā.

Tena saccenasotthite hotusotthigabbhassa.

Sister, since being born in the Noble Birth,
I am not aware that I have intentionally deprived a being of life.
By this truth, may you be well,
and so may the child in your womb.

Lightning Source UK Ltd.
Milton Keynes UK
UKHW020729291219
355991UK00005B/135/P